YOU'RE THE V
Bette Midler

IMP

International MUSIC Publications

© International Music Publications Limited
Griffin House 161 Hammersmith Road London W6 8BS England

Production Editor: Chris Harvey

Editorial, production and recording: Artemis Music Limited
Design: IMP Studio
Photography ©2003 David Redfern / Redferns Music Picture Library

Published 2003

Bette Midler
Born 1945

Born on December 1st, the third daughter of Fred and Ruth Midler, Bette (named by her mother after Bette Davis) was raised in Hawaii where, from an early age, she showed an interest in singing and acting. By the 1960s Midler was living in New York in order to fulfill her dream of becoming a star, and was acting in the long-running Broadway Hit *Fiddler On The Roof*.

In 1972 she signed to Atlantic Records and released *The Divine Miss M*, which became an instant hit, selling over 100,000 copies in the first month alone. The album included a cover version of the Andrews Sisters' *Boogie Woogie Bugle Boy* (which reached the top 10), *The Leader Of The Pack* and *Chapel Of Love*. Her next album, the eponymous *Bette Midler*, in 1973 was equally successful. After a slump in record sales throughout the rest of the seventies, Midler starred in the 1979 film *The Rose*, and the title track became a top ten hit.

However, in 1982 Midler suffered a nervous breakdown after allegations of disagreements between herself and her co-stars in the film *Jinxed*.

She bounced back, though, and her version of *Wind Beneath My Wings* from the film *Beaches* (in which she also starred) reached number one and received a Grammy for 'Record of the Year' in 1989. The soundtrack for the same film, released in 1988, went three times Platinum.

Bette Midler continued producing hits in the nineties, most notably with *Some People's Lives* which was a top ten, million-selling album and included the number two hit *From A Distance*. To date she has released ten studio albums, five soundtracks, a greatest hits album, a comedy album and a live album.

With her determination and unmistakable talent, Bette Midler has had chart success – as well as success with film – for over thirty years. Her ability to remain true to her unique style as well as reflecting the sounds of the time has led to her being a household name as well as one of the most well-respected performers of the twentieth century.

Boogie Woogie Bugle Boy

Words and Music by Don Raye and Hughie Prince

Backing

Chapel Of Love

Words and Music by Phil Spector,
Ellie Greenwich and Jeff Barry

Backing

Lyrics:

1. Spring is here, and the sky is so very blue.
2. Bells will ring, and the sun is gonna shine.

Birds all sing as if they knew
I'm gonna be his, he's gonna be mine.

to - day's the day we'll say, "I do."
We're gon - na love un - til the end of time. And we'll

Friends

Words and Music by Mark Klingman and William Linhart

Track 3
Backing

From A Distance

Words and Music by Julie Gold

3. From a distance, you look like my friend
   Even though we are at war.
   From a distance I just cannot comprehend
   What all this fighting is for.
   From a distance there is harmony
   And it echoes through the land.
   It's the hope of hopes, it's the love of loves.
   It's the heart of every man.

One For My Baby
(And One More For The Road)

Words by Johnny Mercer
Music by Harold Arlen

Backing

Slowly and freely

Hello In There

Words and Music by John Prine

Moderately slow ♩ = 98

1. We had an a - part - ment in the ci - ty,
2. Me and my hus - band, we don't talk much an - y - more.
(Verse 3 see block lyric)

me and my hus - band liked liv - ing there.
He sits and stares through the back door screen.

Verse 3:
So if you're walking down the street sometime
And you should spot some hollow ancient eyes
Don't you pass them by and stare
As if you didn't care.
Say hello in there, hello.

The Rose

Words and Music by Amanda McBroom

Backing

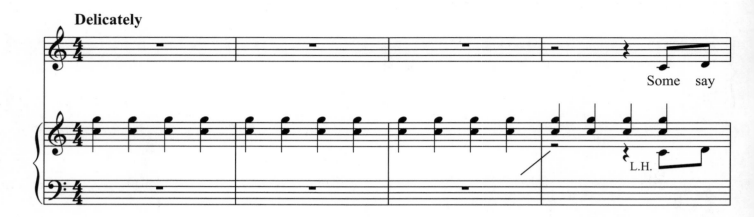

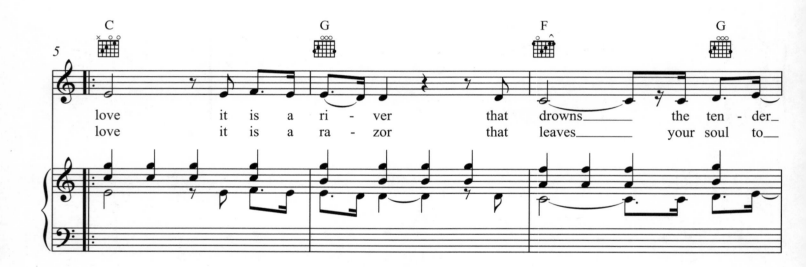

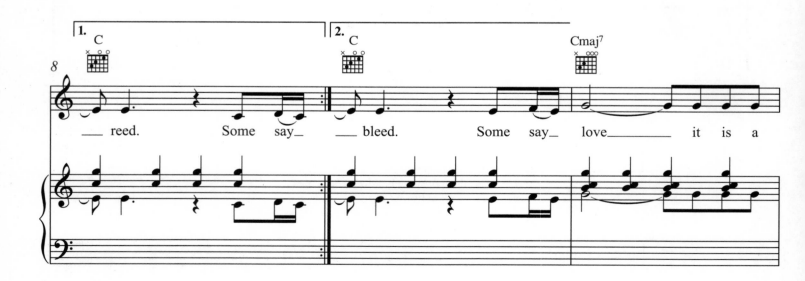

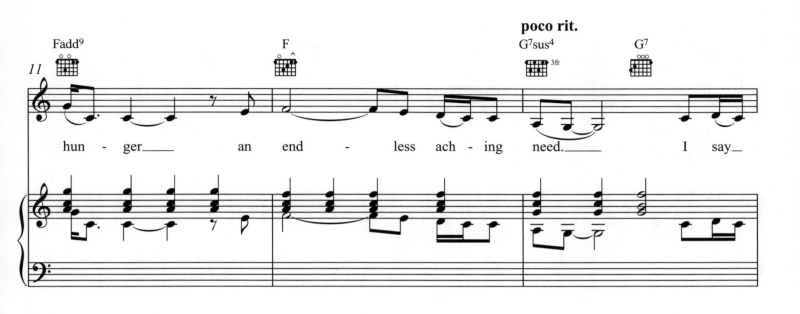

When A Man Loves A Woman

Words and Music by Calvin Lewis and Andrew Wright

Backing

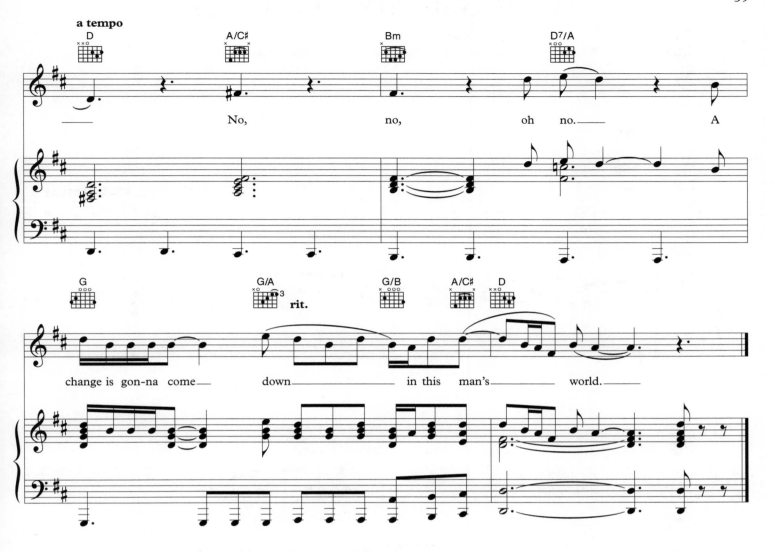

No, no, oh no. A change is gon-na come down in this man's world.

Verse 3:
When a man loves a woman
Down deep in his soul
She can bring him such misery.
Yeah, if she's playin' him for a fool
He's the last one to know
Lovin' eyes don't ever see.

So this man says, "Do you love me?"
Will you give me everything the earth has?
Try to hold on to my precious love
Cryin', "Baby, baby, please don't treat me bad."

Wind Beneath My Wings

Backing

Words and Music by Larry Henley and Jeff Silbar

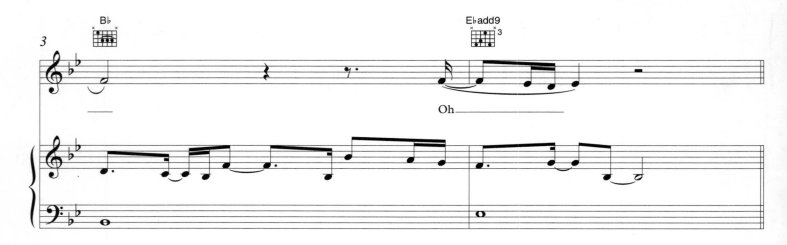

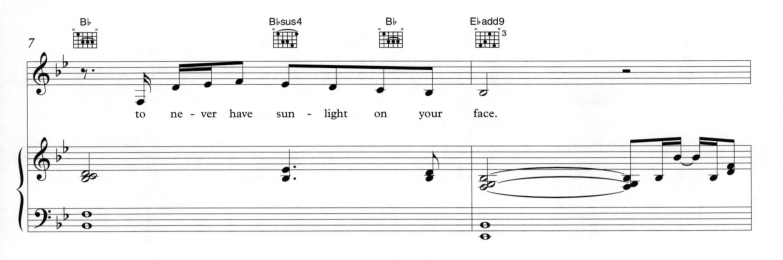

to ne - ver have sun - light on your face.

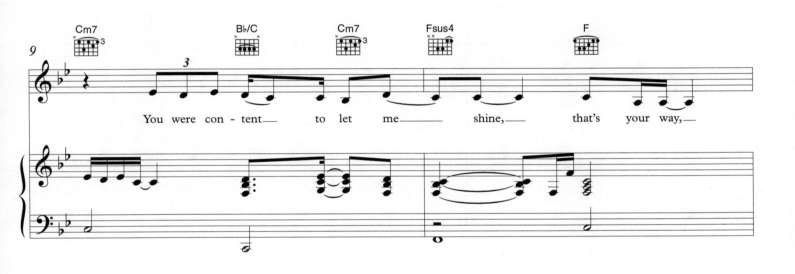

You were con - tent___ to let me___ shine,___ that's your way,___

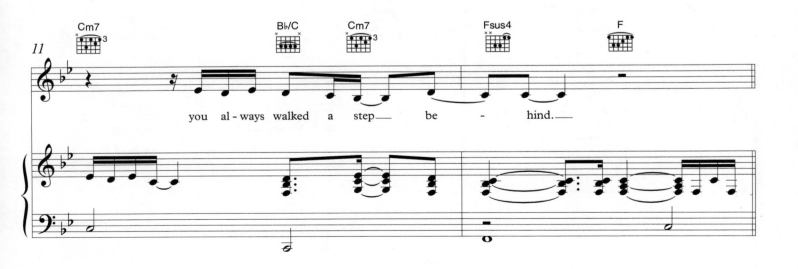

you al - ways walked a step___ be - hind.___

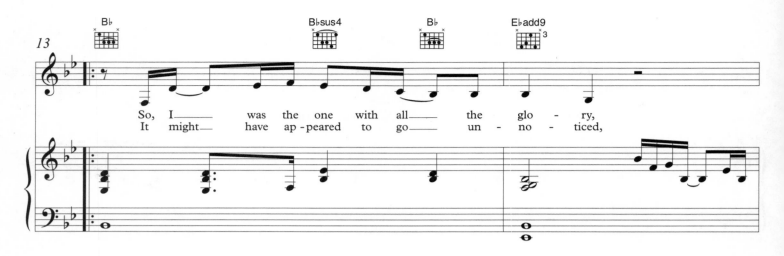

So, I_____ was the one with all_____ the glo - ry,
It might_____ have ap -peared to go_____ un - no - ticed,

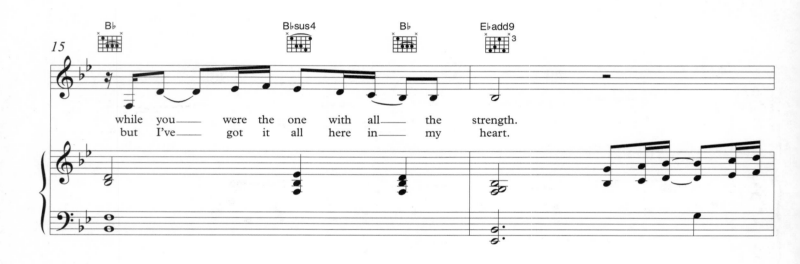

while you_____ were the one with all_____ the strength.
but I've_____ got it all here in_____ my heart.

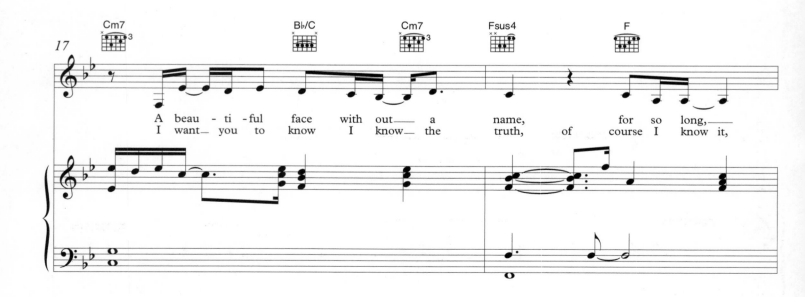

A beau - ti -ful face with out_____ a name, for so long,_____
I want_____ you to know I know_____ the truth, of course I know it,

Only In Miami

Words and Music by Max Gronenthal

Backing

52

And she cries for her child with-out—— a moth-er, and she cries for a

YOU'RE THE VOICE

8861A PV/CD

Casta Diva from Norma - Vissi D'arte from Tosca - Un Bel Di Vedremo from Madam Butterfly - Addio, Del Passato from La Traviata - J'ai Perdu Mon Eurydice from Orphee Et Eurydice - Les Tringles Des Sistres Tintaient from Carmen - Porgi Amor from Le Nozze Di Figaro - Ave Maria from Otello

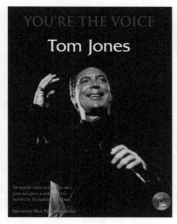

8860A PVG/CD

Delilah - Green Green Grass Of Home - Help Yourself - I'll Never Fall In Love Again - It's Not Unusual - Mama Told Me Not To Come - Sexbomb Thunderball - What's New Pussycat - You Can Leave Your Hat On

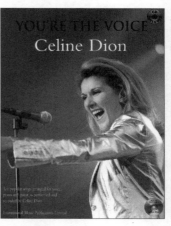

9297A PVG/CD

Beauty And The Beast - Because You Loved Me - Falling Into You - The First Time Ever I Saw Your Face - It's All Coming Back To Me Now - Misled - My Heart Will Go On - The Power Of Love - Think Twice - When I Fall In Love

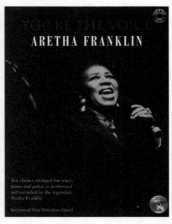

9349A PVG/CD

Chain Of Fools - A Deeper Love Do Right Woman, Do Right Man - I Knew You Were Waiting (For Me) - I Never Loved A Man (The Way I Loved You) I Say A Little Prayer - Respect - Think Who's Zooming Who - (You Make Me Feel Like) A Natural Woman

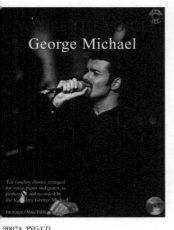

9007A PVG/CD

Careless Whisper - A Different Corner Faith - Father Figure - Freedom '90 I'm Your Man - I Knew You Were Waiting (For Me) - Jesus To A Child Older - Outside

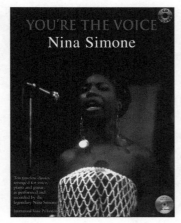

9606A PVG/CD

Don't Let Me Be Misunderstood - Feeling Good - I Loves You Porgy - I Put A Spell On You - Love Me Or Leave Me - Mood Indigo - My Baby Just Cares For Me Ne Me Quitte Pas (If You Go Away) - Nobody Knows You When You're Down And Out - Take Me To The Water

9700A PVG/CD

Beautiful - Crying In The Rain - I Feel The Earth Move - It's Too Late - (You Make Me Feel Like) A Natural Woman So Far Away - Way Over Yonder – Where You Lead - Will You Love Me Tomorrow You've Got A Friend

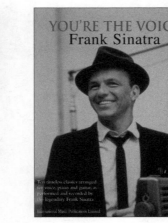

9746A PVG/CD

April In Paris - Come Rain Or Come Shine - Fly Me To The Moon (In Other Words) - I've Got You Under My Skin The Lady Is A Tramp - My Kinda Town (Chicago Is) - My Way Theme From *New York, New York* Someone To Watch Over Me Something Stupid

9770A PVG/CD

Cry Me A River - Evergreen (A Star Is Born) - Happy Days Are Here Again - I've Dreamed Of You - Memory - My Heart Belongs To Me - On A Clear Day (You Can See Forever) - Someday My Prince Will Come - Tell Him (duet with Celine Dion) - The Way We Were

9799A PVG/CD

Boogie Woogie Bugle Boy - Chapel Of Love - Friends - From A Distance - Hello In There - One For My Baby (And One More For The Road) - Only In Miami The Rose - When A Man Loves A Woman Wind Beneath My Wings

The outstanding vocal series from IMP

CD contains full backings for each song, professionally arranged to recreate the sounds of the original recording

  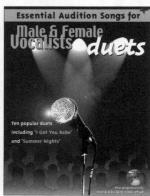 

ESSENTIAL AUDITION SONGS FOR FEMALE VOCALISTS

Broadway

7171A   Book and CD   ISBN: 1859098010

Anything Goes - As Long As He Needs Me - Being Alive - But Not For Me - Fifty Percent - Johnny One Note - Nothing - People - Take Me Or Leave Me - There Won't Be Trumpets

Jazz Standards

7021A   Book and CD   ISBN: 1859097529

Cry Me A River - Desafinado- Ev'ry Time We Say Goodbye - Fever - It's Only A Paper Moon - Mad About The Boy - My Baby Just Cares For Me - Stormy Weather (Keeps Rainin' All The Time) - Summertime - They Can't Take That Away From Me

Pop Ballads

6939A   Book and CD   ISBN: 185909712X

Anything For You - Do You Know Where You're Going To - I Will Always Love You - Killing Me Softly With His - My Heart Will Go On - Over The Rainbow - Promise Me - The Greatest Love Of All- The Way We Were- Walk On By

Pop Divas

7769A   Book and CD   ISBN: 1859099874

Beautiful Stranger - Believe - Genie In A Bottle - I Don't Want To Wait - I Try - Pure Shores - The Greatest Love Of All- Un-Break My Heart - Waiting For Tonight - Without You

ESSENTIAL AUDITION SONGS FOR MALE VOCALISTS

Broadway

9185A   Book and CD   ISBN: 1843280124

Don't Get Around Much Anymore - From Sophisticated Ladies - Get Me To The Church On Time From My Fair Lady - If I Were A Rich Man From Fiddler On The Roof - It Don't Mean A Thing (If It Ain't Got That Swing) From Sophisticated Ladies - It's All Right With Me From Can-Can - On The Street Where You Live From My Fair Lady - Thank Heaven For Little Girls From Gigi - The Lady Is A Tramp From Babes In Arms - Wandrin' Star From Paint Your Wagon - With A Little Bit Of Luck From My Fair Lady

Crooners

9495A   Book and CD   ISBN: 1843280922

Can't Take My Eyes Off You - I Left My Heart In San Francisco - Mack The Knife - My Way - Swingin' On A Star - The Way We Were - Theme From 'New York, New York' - (What A) Wonderful World - When I Fall In Love - Volare

ESSENTIAL AUDITION SONGS FOR FEMALE & MALE VOCALISTS

Duets

7432A   Book and CD   ISBN: 1859099009

Barcelona - Don't Go Breaking My Heart - Endless Love - I Got You Babe - I Knew You Were Waiting (For Me) - (I've Had) The Time Of My Life - It Takes Two - Kids - Nothing's Gonna Stop Us Now - Summer Nights

Essential Audition Songs For Kids

7341A   Book and CD   ISBN: 1859098673

Bugsy Malone - Consider Yourself Love's Got A Hold On My Heart Maybe This Time - My Favourite Things - My Name Is Tallulah The Rainbow - We're In The Money Wouldn't It Be Loverly - You're Fully Dressed Without A Smile

Essential Audition Songs For Wannabe Pop Stars

9735A   Book and CD   ISBN: 1843282453

Angels - Anything Is Possible - Back For Good - Ev'ry Time We Say Goodbye - Flying Without Wings - Genie In A Bottle - Get Happy - Reach - Up On The Roof - Whole Again